Stick in the Mud

Sally Farrell Odgers

illustrated by Moira Laidlaw

Modern Curriculum Press
Cleveland and Toronto

Once, there was a man named Stick. He was a cross and grumpy man, and he was a mean man, too! He used to put all his money in a big fat bag and carry it with him wherever he went. He had so much money that he needed both arms to carry it. Oh, it was heavy! And that made Stick crosser than ever.

One day, Stick decided to walk to the market to see what bargains he could buy. It was a wonderful warm day, but it had been raining all through the night. Because Stick was carrying his moneybag in front of him, he didn't see the large mud puddle in the middle of the road.

Splat! Down he sat!
"Drat!" said Stick, and because he was afraid to put down
his moneybag he couldn't get himself out of the mud.

While Stick was sitting in the mud, a farmer came along the road.

"What's the matter with you?" asked the farmer.

"I'm stuck," said Stick, and he scowled.

"I'll try and pull you out," said the farmer. He put down his hoe and got hold of Stick by the shoulders, and he pulled and pulled — but Stick still stayed stuck in the mud. "Well, I don't know!" said the farmer.

Just then, a teacher came along the road.
"What's the matter with Stick?" she asked.
"Stick-in-the-mud is stuck in the mud, and how shall we
get him out?" said the farmer. "I've tried pulling him
out."

"Have you tried pushing him out?" asked the teacher. She put down her books and pressed her hands against Stick's back, and she pushed and pushed — but Stick still stayed stuck in the mud.

"Well, I'm sure I don't know!" said the teacher.

The next person to come along the road was a fisherman.
''What's the matter with Stick?'' he asked.
''Stick-in-the-mud is stuck in the mud, and how shall we
get him out?'' said the farmer and the teacher.
''I've tried pulling him out,'' said the farmer.
''And I've tried pushing him out,'' said the teacher.

"Ah," said the fisherman. "But have you tried fishing him out?" He hooked his biggest fishhook into the back of Stick's trousers, and picked up his fishing rod. He began to reel in the line. He reeled and reeled and the rod bent like a bow, but Stick still stayed stuck in the mud.
"Blimey! I dunno!" said the fisherman.

Along came a salesman with a case of samples to sell at the
market. "What's the matter with Stick?" he asked.
"Stick-in-the-mud is stuck in the mud and how shall we get
him out?" said the farmer, the teacher and the fisherman.
"I've tried pulling him out," said the farmer.
"I've tried pushing him out," said the teacher.
"And I've tried fishing him out," said the fisherman.

"Hmm," said the salesman, opening his case. "I wonder if you've tried tempting him out?"
He took out a wonderful gadget and held it in front of Stick, just out of reach. "It's very good value for the money, and guaranteed to make you richer than ever!" murmured the salesman. Stick leaned forward, and reached for the gadget with one finger, but Stick still stayed stuck in the mud.
"Oh, well," said the salesman, and he put the gadget away in his case.

Then, along the road drove a road worker.
''What's the matter with Stick?'' asked the road worker,
jumping down from his bulldozer.
''Stick-in-the-mud is stuck in the mud, and how shall we
get him out?'' said the farmer, the teacher, the fisherman
and the salesman.
''I've tried pulling him out,'' said the farmer.
''I've tried pushing him out,'' said the teacher.
''I've tried fishing him out,'' said the fisherman.
''And I've tried tempting him out,'' said the salesman.

"Ah, but have you tried bulldozing him out?" asked the road worker. He jumped back onto his bulldozer and drove slowly toward Stick. He bulldozed and bulldozed — but Stick still stayed stuck in the mud.
"Bad luck," said the road worker.

Then they all heard a loud noise. *Tar-a-ta-TA!* And along the road came a trumpeter.

"What's the matter with Stick?" asked the trumpeter, wiping her trumpet on her skirt.

"Stick-in-the-mud is stuck in the mud and how shall we get him out?" said the farmer, the teacher, the fisherman, the salesman and the road worker.

"I've tried pulling him out," said the farmer.

"I've tried pushing him out," said the teacher.

"I've tried fishing him out," said the fisherman.

"I've tried tempting him out," said the salesman.

"I've tried bulldozing him out," said the road worker.

"Hmph!" said the trumpeter. "I bet you haven't tried blowing him out!" She handed her trumpet to the teacher and went up to Stick. She drew a deep, deep breath, held it — and then she *blewewew!* Stick's hair streamed sideways and his ears turned blue with cold, but Stick still stayed stuck in the mud.

"Whew!" said the trumpeter.

Up jogged a football player in a striped sweater and boots.
"What's the matter with Stick?" asked the football player
jerkily.
"Stick-in-the-mud is stuck in the mud and how shall we get
him out?" said the farmer, the teacher, the fisherman, the
salesman, the road worker and the trumpeter.
"I've tried pulling him out," said the farmer.
"I've tried pushing him out," said the teacher.
"I've tried fishing him out," said the fisherman.
"I've tried tempting him out," said the salesman.
"I've tried bulldozing him out," said the road worker.
"And I've tried blowing him out," said the trumpeter.

"Huh! Tried kicking him out?" asked the football player as he swung back one big boot and kicked Stick right in the seat of his pants.

"Ow!" yelled Stick.

But Stick still stayed stuck in the mud.

While they were all standing around, a thief came by. She
was small and dainty, with a black mask over her face.
''Pst!'' said the thief, peering cautiously past the football
player. ''What's the matter with Stick?''
''Stick-in-the-mud is stuck in the mud and how shall we get
him out?'' said the farmer, the teacher, the fisherman, the
salesman, the road worker, the trumpeter and the football
player.
''I've tried pulling him out,'' sighed the farmer.
''And I've tried pushing him out,'' nodded the teacher.
''I've tried fishing him out,'' agreed the fisherman.
''I've tried tempting him out,'' said the salesman.
''I've tried bulldozing him out,'' said the road worker.
''I've tried blowing him out,'' complained the trumpeter.
''I've tried kicking him out,'' puffed the football player,
jogging.

The thief thought.
"I wonder if you've tried stealing him out?" she asked
gently.

"Who'd want to steal Stick?" wondered the farmer.
"He's impolite," said the teacher.
"He's a grump," said the fisherman.
"He's hard to get on with," said the salesman.
"He's tough," said the road worker.
"He's ungrateful," said the trumpeter.
"He's lazy," said the football player.
"He's a Stick-in-the-mud!" they all said together. "And he's **mean**!"

The thief nodded, and smiled under her mask. ''Good!''
she said, and she slipped around the other side of the
puddle and grabbed Stick's moneybag out of his arms.
Stick-in-the-mud shot out of the mud like a rocket.

"Stop thief!" roared Stick, and chased after the thief with the farmer, the teacher, the fisherman, the salesman, the road worker, the trumpeter and the football player running behind.

Of course they didn't catch her.

But as they reached the market, they found the moneybag waiting on the side of the road.

Stick snatched it up.

''Bet you won't carry that around with you after this!'' said the farmer.

''Won't I?'' glared Stick.

''But what if you fall in the mud again?'' wondered the trumpeter.

Stick snorted. ''I'll take the other road home. Get going all of you!''